CW01064969

Brigitte Lunguieki Malungo

If My Skin Could Talk

story.one – Life is a story

 story.one

1st edition 2023
© Brigitte Lunguieki Malungo

Production, design and conception:
story.one publishing - www.story.one
A brand of Storylution GmbH

Font set from Minion Pro, Lato and Merriweather.

© Cover photo: Mayamba Gomes

© Photos: Abigail Edele (https://linkfro.de/abbysoul)

Translated by Amrah Gadziev // Editing and Proofreading by Meydi Urtecho and Hannah Koinig (https://www.lektoratbutterblume.com)

ISBN: 978-3-7108-7957-9

I wrote these intimate, candid, poignant, and redemptive verses, unbridled and drawn straight from the depths of my being.

And in crafting them, I did so with you, my dear reader, in mind.

Let us now resound with fervor, and may our voices never again be hushed to silence!

CONTENT

"As a Black woman, my daily existence is fraught with the specter of racism, microaggressions, colorism, and various forms of discrimination"

Preface

The composition *If My Skin Could Talk* proved to be an arduous endeavor. Throughout the writing process, I found myself shedding countless tears, necessitating occasional breaks to regain composure. Before delving further, I feel compelled to issue a trigger warning, for within these short stories, one shall encounter vivid depictions of physical violence among other topics.

I wish to emphasize that my intention is not to lay blame or evoke excessive emotions; rather, I aspire to provoke introspection. These narratives invite contemplation regarding behavioral patterns and the immense impact of seemingly innocuous words when carelessly chosen. Moreover, I seek to bring attention to the privilege associated with being white.

To emphasize a shared connection of experiences with racism, I have deliberately capitalized the term »Black« in my book. Its usage transcends mere description of ethnicity or skin color, serving as an emblem of political self-empowerment for Black individuals.

Conversely, »white« remains in lowercase, representing a reference to social positioning within the broader context of a global power structure, as exemplified by Germany's white-dominated social order. (Source: Aydemir, Fatma et al.(2020): Eure Heimat ist unser Albtraum. Ullstein Buchverlage, Berlin, 8th edition).

Considering terminology, I have been questioned on appropriate references for individuals with darker skin. Acceptable terms include »Black« and »BIPoC« (Black, Indigenous, and People of Color). On a personal level, I firmly disavow the term »colored«. Naturally, it goes without saying that the usage of the N-word is unequivocally unacceptable.

For me *If My Skin Could Talk* serves as a reflection of my past, my present, and lamentably, an apprehensive glimpse into my future.

As a Black woman, my daily existence is fraught with the specter of racism, microaggressions, colorism, and various forms of discrimination – an inescapable reality that spurred the necessity and significance of this literary work. My fervent belief is that this book's message bears equal necessity and importance for me and the world.

> **66** From a height of ten meters, his dreams of making the world a better place came crashing down with him, extinguished in an instant **99**

Rest in peace, Mbutu

On that frigid January night, when the moon cast an icy glow upon the desolate streets, a tragedy befell Mbutu, the older brother of my dear friend.

Brutally assaulted, he suffered a merciless beating before being callously hurled from a bridge.

The impact as his head met the unyielding ground echoed with the sickening sound of bones shattering. In an instant, crimson blood mingled with the pristine snow, and his brain matter spilled forth, silently absorbed by the deep drifts.

Glimmers of darkness cloaked the assailants, four shadowy figures clad in black jackets, their presence ominous against the dim night. Black boots, laced with white, delivered relentless blows, rending his skin and leaving behind a trail of crimson.

A thick tape muzzled his anguished cries, imprisoning the screams within.

Yet, even stifled, the torment seared through him, and he could do naught but scream into the void within his being. Breath became scarce, yet his wails persisted, unrestrained.

His tears, however, streamed freely from his weakened frame, flowing ceaselessly – his last offering from tearful eyes now forever stilled.

At dawn's emergence, fate led a man walking his dog to the harrowing scene. The big shepherd, sensing distress, rushed to the motionless figure clad in black against the sea of white. Instinctively, the dog sought to comfort the young man, sniffing and licking his face.

But the reality that greeted them was far graver. Mbutu lay lifeless, his eyes wide with unspoken horror, limbs contorted unnaturally.

His attackers had left him stripped bare, a gruesome mark etched on his breast – an emblematic cross, each arm bent at a right angle.

The walker collapsed in dismay, arched his back in agony and vomited in great quantities next to Mbutu. Still trembling, he managed to dial the emergency number, though he knew no aid could restore Mbutu's stolen life.

From a height of ten meters, his dreams of making the world a better place came crashing down with him, extinguished in an instant. No emergency call could alter this cruel reality.

"

Dirty

African

fingers

"

Coffee is made early in the morning

»Here you go, an espresso macchiato, a pretzel roll with salami and a raisin bun to go.« My warm smile accompanied the careful placement of the tray, adorned with a paper cup and neatly wrapped pastries, upon the counter. »Your total amounts to six euros and ninety-eight cents. Will you be paying with cash or by card?« I inquired with unwavering geniality. The lady, likely in her fifties, adjusted her vibrant red glasses, their lenses magnifying her gaze, and stared back at me without uttering a word.

Attempting to decipher the depths of her gaze proved perplexing. Was she taken aback by the price, perhaps still drowsy at this early hour, unable to hear my question? Or was her hesitation linked to an underlying discomfort with being served by a Black woman? Sadly, such scenarios were all too common, transpiring almost daily, and despite the frequency, I found no fortitude in facing them.

Yesterday, my experienced coworker, Annelore, and I manned the sales counter together. An older man had the audacity to repeatedly admonish me against touching his coffee cup with what he crudely referred to as my »dirty African fingers«, loudly insisting on being attended to solely by my coworker. Annelore responded curtly, asserting, »Mr. Kirschhaus, as you can observe, my hands are occupied. If you refuse the service of my esteemed colleague and continue to insult individuals here, I must insist that you promptly depart our bakery. What shall be your choice?« Annoyed and grumbling inaudibly, he turned on his heels, leaving us to hear fragments of his discontent: »This cannot be...customer is always right...I come here every...« We exchanged knowing glances, our patience waning.

»If you hadn't intervened, I would have given him a piece of my mind«, I confessed, my voice trembling, as Annelore gently touched my arm. »I understand, and you would have been entirely justified, but I didn't want him to further spoil your day«, she reassured me with a kind smile, for which I felt immensely grateful.

Today, standing alone behind the counter, I braced myself for yet another potential altercation that might echo from the expansive windows. However, the lady with the conspicuous spectacles remained silent, gazing unwaveringly at me. Eventually, she averted her eyes, retrieving her purse from her handbag to settle the bill with a ten euro note. I accepted it gracefully, placing the change upon a metal tray before her. »Here you go, have a wonderful day«, I said, earnestly hoping to bring closure to this peculiar moment.

Unexpectedly, the corners of her lips twitched. »Thank you, and the same to you. Your German is remarkably proficient«, she expressed her astonishment, her immense eyes focused intently on me. With an amiable smile, I replied, »Thank you, and yours as well.« As she left the bakery, equally bewildered and evidently offended, I found myself softly chuckling.

Apartment-Hunting

During my early childhood, I found myself sharing a room with my two sisters, and the novelty of our companionship proved quite delightful. Bedtime became an enchanting ritual as I wove captivating tales, relishing the opportunity to come up with spine-chilling narratives that left their hearts pounding with excitement. Beneath the veil of darkness, they listened intently to the soft cadence of my whispers. Whenever our vigilant parents stealthily approached the bedroom door to ascertain if we had succumbed to slumber, we adeptly feigned stillness, adhering to an unspoken code of silence. Yet, our sisterhood was to undergo a significant change with the arrival of a new addition: a mere nine-month-old sibling, claiming her spot within our room. Night after night, her plaintive cries jolted us awake, disrupting our peaceful rest. The loss of my private space filled me with discontent, but what followed was far more alarming. One fateful night, the bunk bed, under the strain of our collective slumber, collapsed without warning. I found myself trapped beneath the weight of the slatted frame and my elder sister's mattress, struggling to draw breath, a moment of terror that seared into my memory. The necessity for a more spacious abode and sturdier beds became irrefutably apparent.

In a concerted effort, we helped our parents in the search for a new dwelling, meticulously poring over newspaper ads, marking promising listings with a vibrant marker. Despite our earnest endeavors, no affordable apartments surfaced within the vicinity. In a last-ditch attempt, my father enlisted the services of a real estate agent, and after a brief wait, he secured a viewing appointment for a luminous and expansive 5-room apartment. Accompanied by my parents, we ascended to the ninth floor, where I had already staked a claim on the largest room, brimming with excitement. However, the joviality faded when the landlord opened the door and upon sighting us, his smile vanished, replaced by a frigid indifference. Ignoring my father's outstretched hand, he exchanged a curt handshake with the real estate agent. A premonitory shiver raced down my spine, foretelling the impending disappointment of our visit.

Our quest persisted, my parents forging ahead independently. I happened upon a conversation overheard through a partly opened door. Initially promising, the dialogue delved into salaries and potential move-in dates, indicating that a viewing might soon be arranged. Then came the landlady's abrupt inquiry, shattering all optimism. »You're Germans, aren't you?«, she probed. In response, my father's Adam's apple bobbed, his voice faltered as he shared our heritage, originating from Angola, a country nestled southwest of...

»That settles it then. I'd rather set my apartment on fire than rent it to Africans«, the landlady retorted gruffly, hanging up without remorse. Horror and speechlessness marred my father's countenance as my mother clasped her hands in a gesture of silent prayer. A lone tear trailed down my cheek, emblematic of the pain wrought by the senseless prejudices we encountered.

" Hello chocolate candy, when do I get to unwrap you? "
asked Oscar, 37, three days ago. Needless to say, the match fizzled out swiftly

Of chocolate and candy

Familiar to all are the terms of endearment, those affectionate nicknames bestowed upon loved ones in place of their given names. Honey, Hon, Darling, Baby, and Babe top the list, followed by the more whimsical Bae, Boo, or Buttercup. Endearments such as Cutie Pie, Peach, Sugar Plum, and even the peculiar Honey Cup find their place in the lexicon. Notably, these tend to be food-related, often prefaced with the word »little«. The possessive pronoun »my« frequently precedes them, as in My Lil' Darling, My Lil' Sugar Plum, or My Babe. Personally, I find no appeal in such pet names. But let's not dwell on that.

As I continue my ventures into dating apps, the primary benefactors of my mobile data, I find myself confronted with some matches who opt to greet me with a cheery »Hola bombón« in their initial messages. There's a certain charm to it, I must admit. I've always adored the Spanish language, which I wisely chose as an elective during my high school days. If only

Spanish could become a relaxing oasis, a soothing bath to submerge myself in whenever I seek refuge from life's negativity and burdens. Alas, back to the subject at hand.

For those who haven't yet indulged, I must kindly implore you to Google the translation of the beguiling nickname »bombón«. Unsurprisingly, the search results promptly unveil a variety of chocolate and confectionary-related terms.

»Hello chocolate candy, when do I get to unwrap you?« asked Óscar, 37, three days ago. Needless to say, the match fizzled out swiftly.

»Hello chocolate, what color are your nipples?« inquired Andrés, 34, today. Humanity, it seems, is more lost than I imagined.

»Hi there, chocolate candy, I love the color of your skin. If we meet, I'll prove to you that I, too, am Black at heart« asserted Maca, 31, yesterday. How she plans to substantiate such an absurd claim, I cannot fathom.

»Hello chocolate, can I lick you?« queried Iván, 29, the day before yesterday. I was rendered utterly speechless.

Regrettably, these types of messages have become an all too frequent occurrence on dating apps, leaving me thoroughly exasperated. The sheer magnitude of ignorance and absurdity bundled into a single communication is almost comical. Is this truly happening? Did my match genuinely believe that such a message would suffice, or were they simply devoid of all reason? One cannot seriously expect messages of this ilk to spark ongoing conversations or, heaven forbid, flatter the recipient. Or can they? The dating world has become an enigma to me. But enough for today; I shall retire for a soothing bath. Farewell for now.

The bucket list

I sense the rhythmic throb of my heartbeat against my tongue as Jorge's intense gaze connects with mine. His piercing eyes possess an uncanny ability to render my legs weak and trembling, akin to being embraced by a delightful sense of vulnerability. My stomach flutters like a gathering of delicate ants, each one performing an agile limbo dance. The allure becomes overpowering, and I find myself straddling his lap, my fingers entwined in the silken strands of his hair.

With a delicate gesture, I caress the tip of my tongue against the contour of his lower lip, invitingly. Our mutual desire ignites like a tempest, and he willingly allows my fervent tongue to venture inside the confines of his mouth, exploring its every hidden recess. Jorge clutches my waist, drawing me closer to him, and I become acutely aware of his arousal pressing tantalizingly against my tender core.

A wistful smile graces my lips as I indulge in reminiscence. At a certain juncture, we found ourselves entwined, our bodies unclothed, and Jorge's tender touch left imprints akin to warm embers upon my skin. His chilled nose nestled in the curve of my neck, while his athletic frame rested heavily upon mine, exuding a comforting warmth.

Today, Instagram serves as a poignant reminder that he now revels in the coffee-growing region of Colombia, entangled in the company of a dark-haired beauty. Witnessing their numerous Stories, capturing moments of shared intimacy, beachside escapades, and road trips, elicits a pang of pain within me. I have relinquished the notion of accompanying him to Machu Picchu in Peru, as his abrupt voice message extinguished any such possibilities. Unexpectedly, it shook the very foundation beneath my feet, leaving me disoriented.

Had I been naively taken advantage of during those two months when we shared an inexplicably close connection? Was I reduced to a mere item on his bucket list, a Black woman he desired solely for some fetishized experience? The apprehension settles in, and I discern the telltale signs now, the suggestive remarks he made.

»I won't be able to be with a white woman again«, or »Your skin is irresistible. I'm captivated by it.«

In the throes of passion, these words seemed benign, but upon retrospection, their underlying bitterness becomes evident. Why couldn't he have simply said, »I cherish being with you« or »I'm genuinely captivated by you«? Why this fixation on my skin color?

These ruminations weigh heavily on my mind, and I wonder if I'm alone in grappling with such thoughts. Whenever I engage in intimacy with someone who is not Black, the unsettling question persists: Am I merely a mere object of curiosity, a fetishized experiment? My heart constricts painfully as I confront these emotions, seeking a way to transcend them.

"Nutella, come here." Markus called out yesterday, his words inflicting a queasy sensation within me

Nutella for breakfast

My heart leaps with pure adoration for Nutella – an unrivaled passion that enchants my taste buds with its delicious sweetness, whether gracing freshly baked, hearty country-style bread or savored straight from the jar with a spoon. Our pantry, ever abundant with several jars, testifies to its allure, cherished not only by me but by my entire family. When Mom and Dad's watchful eyes momentarily stray, I take the chance to generously spread Nutella on my bread, reveling in its delectable richness before they catch on and reprimand me. Deep down, I know Nutella isn't the healthiest choice, but it's too irresistible to resist.

The colossal 750g jar bears a composition of pure sugar and ecologically detrimental palm oil, supplemented by skimmed milk powder, a dash of cocoa, and a sprinkling of hazelnuts. Nonetheless, none of this diminishes its status as my absolute favorite treat, and I diligently brush my teeth afterwards, striving for balance. I even experimented once, dipping cold fries from the previous day into the jar, and the result was remarkably delicious, surpassing the conventional ketchup or mayo. Alas, such clandestine exploits were essential, for Mom insists that Nutella should only accompany bread or pastries, a perspective that occasionally irks me. Nutella, in my view, complements everything with utmost ease, with the exception of fish and meat – a culinary mystery I am eager to explore further.

As part of my daily ritual, I relish two slices of country-style bread adorned with Nutella for breakfast, convinced that this cherished routine would remain unchanging, carrying me into my elderly years. However, in recent days, a sour feeling bubbles within me whenever the jar graces the dining room table, and the cause of my discomfort is none other than Markus, the most popular boy in my class, perhaps even the entire elementary school.

»Nutella, come here«, Markus called out yesterday, his words inflicting a queasy sensation within me. It all began a week ago when he first christened me with that name, quickly embraced by his followers. Each utterance stings, and I mustered the courage to confront him, questioning the reason behind his hurtful words. His response, a sneer that pierced my heart, lingered in my mind, »Have you looked at yourself in the mirror?«

Mom's daily inquiries about my school day always invite a familiar response of »Good.« However, one instance led me to provide a different answer, revealing that Markus had extended invitations to his birthday party, with one glaring exception – me. The notion of being excluded based on the term »Nutellas« pained my mother, and witnessing her sadness shattered my heart. From that moment on, I vowed to protect her from any further disappointment, responding with a simple »Good« regardless of the reality of my school days, which seldom align with the facade I project. As a result, I stand resolved to make myself a Nutella sandwich tomorrow morning, just like always, a comforting ritual that symbolizes the steadfast love I have for my mother and the desire to shield her from any sadness.

"Why did you automatically assume I was the new cleaning lady?"

New job

With a tinge of despair, I cast my gaze upon the daunting mound of clothes piled up on my bed. Nervously, I have been pacing back and forth for what seems like an eternity, continuously changing outfits in a fervent pursuit of the perfect combination. Eventually, I settle upon outfit number eight, a mustard-yellow blouse with puffed sleeves complementing the black and white checkered pants. My reflection in the mirror earns a nod of approval, granting this attire the privilege of accompanying me on my inaugural day at the new job. Time, however, urges me forward, and I hurriedly apply light makeup and a spritz of perfume to my neck and décolleté before hastily departing the apartment.

Upon my arrival at the new school, I am met with a disheartening discovery – unsightly sweat stains mar the armpits of my blouse. Regret gnaws at me for not changing into a fresh blouse at home or rectifying the situation in the restroom. Alas, such thoughts are futile, as the opportunity has now passed. As I wave my arms, hoping to hasten the drying process, I almost allow the door to close behind me, but a petite white woman interjects swiftly, propping the door ajar with her foot. I extend a courtesy by holding the door open for her, and in gratitude, she graces me with a beaming smile. Introducing herself as Eva Weger, we soon discover that today marks the first day at work for both of us.

The receptionist, seemingly bored with her fashion magazine, glances up as we greet her. I offer my name first, followed by Eva. Displaying a glacial pace and visible indifference, she eventually picks up the telephone receiver and speaks into it after a few ponderous moments. »Hello Maria, the new cleaning lady Brigitte Malungo has just arrived.« Confusion fills me, and I attempt to signal vehemently with my arm and index finger that there has been a mixup. Yet, before I can utter a word, Maria seems to have resolved the matter, as evidenced by the color draining from the receptionist's face.

»Oh...yes...I see...I thought she was the new...yes, Mrs. Weger is here, too...yes, she's waiting for you here.«

Without deigning to give us another glance, the receptionist dials another number, informing my future colleague, Mr. Heiner, who teaches Maths and PE, that I await him in the entrance hall. As she bids him farewell, she retreats into her fashion magazine with a crimson flush coloring her cheeks. Unable to restrain myself, I inquire, »Why did you automatically assume I was the new cleaning lady? Is it solely due to my ethnicity – the fact that I am Black?« She pointedly averts her gaze, refusing to respond. In that silence, I discern the unspoken truth, and it is clear we shall never become friends.

"

...suggesting that my German identity is somehow invalidated due to the color of my skin

"

Where are you really from?

With a tingling sense of anticipation, I grasp the door handle firmly, briefly closing my eyes to collect myself with a deep breath. Mr. Heiner, the teacher who escorted me to the entrance hall, was called away, leaving me to stand nervously before the faculty lounge. My heart beats uncontrollably in my chest, and I can't fathom the reason behind my heightened anxiety. After all, this isn't my first teaching position. The school, boasting state-of-the-art whiteboards and a diverse range of extracurricular activities, including ballet and robotics, holds a coveted status as one of the most sought-after bilingual elementary schools in the country. Here, children not only speak German and English but also receive instruction in Spanish and French.

Curiosity compels me to wonder about the people behind the door. How will my new colleagues welcome me? Will they regard me with disdain, akin to the receptionist? Is it possible to form meaningful connections and friendships here? Moreover, a question weighs heavily on my heart: Will I finally encounter other Black teachers within these halls? With a renewed focus, I open my eyes and grasp the opulent gold-plated door handle, venturing forth without further contemplation.

Inside, warm greetings and enthusiastic handshakes ensue as we take our places around the elongated table. One man, seemingly in his late thirties, appraises me with an enigmatic expression gracing his features. His first inquiry takes me aback, as I wouldn't have asked such a question right from the outset. Instead of inquiring about my journey or teaching subjects, he asks, »So, tell us, where are you from?« The line of questioning strikes me as peculiar, making me slightly uncomfortable. It seems as though they must categorize me based on preconceived notions before engaging in genuine conversation. Reserving judgment, I calmly reply, »From Germany.« However, his insistence echoes in the adverb »No, where are you *really* from?« suggesting that my German identity is somehow invalidated due to the color of my skin. I maintain composure and offer, »From Weinstadt, near Stuttgart«, reluctant to divulge my entire life story. An air of disdain accompanies his raised eyebrow and crossed arms, deepening my discomfort, yet he remains silent.

In present times, when posed with the same inquiry, I choose to state that I was born in Angola and raised in Germany. And sometimes people are satisfied with that answer and don't try to evict me from being German or poke around in my intimate, if only small, identity crisis.

Magic hair

Today, the arrival of a new classmate stirs anticipation within me. As I watch the empty seat beside me, brimming with excitement, I hold a glimmer of hope that she might become my first true best friend. In the nights leading up to this moment, I've lain awake, weaving images of her in my mind. A vision ensues, as if painted by the portrayal of ninety-five percent of girls gracing the TV or adorning the pages of my children's books – blond, straight hair cascading down to her shoulders, and eyes akin to the captivating hue of the sea. Even my Barbie dolls embody that very appearance. In moments of fantasy, I often yearn for a transformation like Cinderella, wishing to mirror this idealized beauty, hoping it might halt the incessant stares that follow me – at school, the supermarket, the pediatrician's office, and the playground – piercing gazes that etch themselves on my skin.

Yet, destiny unfolds in a way I could never have foreseen. Beatriz, our new classmate, makes her entrance, and my breath catches in my throat. Beatriz, like me, is Black, but she bears a uniqueness that sets her apart. Unlike the course my mother chooses for my hair – a chemical straightening process that brings pain and discomfort – Beatriz proudly flaunts her tightly curled, dark brown hair, a crown of glory framing her petite countenance. My mother has long deemed Afro hair as unsightly and burdensome, leading to the destruction of my own natural curls with chemical substances.

As Beatriz approaches, I can't help but shoot her an irate glare, my initial instinct resisting her proximity with her exuberant, untamed locks. The other kids cast their curious gazes our way, a common occurrence for me, but this time their expressions reflect equal bewilderment at Beatriz's presence.

Undeterred by the scrutiny, Beatriz takes her place beside me, gracing me with a joyous wink that emanates warmth. Her dark brown eyes glimmer, and endearing dimples grace her cheeks. In that instant, my heart softens, and I find myself inexplicably drawn to her despite her unconventional hair. In the days that follow, Beatriz surprises us all with an array of hairstyles: two cute braids reminiscent of Minnie Mouse, a wonderfully colorful headscarf playfully showcasing her hair, twists, and Bantu knots, each week unveiling a new expression of her magical Afro hair. I am captivated, deeply fascinated by the beauty of her ever-changing styles.

Having come to know more about hair types, Beatriz informs me that my hair also falls into the category of Type 4C, with its fine zigzag curls. She enlightens me, sharing her wisdom, and most notably, she never succumbs to the allure of straightening her hair, understanding the damage it inflicts upon our cherished curls. My admiration for her grows, and I long to impart this newfound knowledge to my mother, hoping to sway her perception. Perhaps one day, Beatriz's mother can speak with her, shedding light on the true beauty of our natural curls.

"You're pretty for a Black girl"

To my Black siblings

Have you ever experienced the haunting sensation of not belonging, of being the sole Black individual in spaces such as elementary school, university, or a social gathering? The intense scrutiny, as if you were an exotic rarity, an outsider from a far-off land, or a creature confined to a zoo exhibit – a spectacle for others' curious amusement. I recall the first time I was struck with the venomous sting of the phrase »Go back to your country«, an unwarranted assault on my young heart at the tender age of eight. Back then, the true weight of those hateful words might not have fully registered, but as time has passed, they linger in my memory, evoking a visceral ache that echoes deep within.

Have you ever been subjected to the humiliating act of someone purposefully switching seats in a train, offering you a scornful look as they relocate? I can still vividly remember the last occurrence, the heaviness that settled upon my heart, threatening to unleash torrents of tears that I struggled to contain. With every instance, I endeavored to shield myself, to let their malice and disgust ricochet off my seemingly impervious exterior. Yet, a breaking point arrived, and the thick armor that I wore appeared feeble, riddled with cracks through which painful encounters and hurtful words effortlessly penetrated.

Have you ever borne witness, as a young girl, to a white mother who, in response to her child asking »Mom, why is that girl so black?«, she nonchalantly responded, »Oh, she's been out in the sun for too long«, and she would flash you a sly wink while leisurely brushing through your hair?

How many times have you encountered the tiresome refrain that all Black women possess a »big ass«, »full lips«, and an innate talent for dancing? How many eye rolls and exasperated sighs have you stifled in response, feeling a mix of annoyance and sheer exhaustion?

How do you react when confronted with social media posts depicting violent attacks on Black individuals? The news of Black folks enduring brutal beatings, torture, shootings, killings, and burnings pierces my soul with each exposure. The weight of the hatred becomes almost unbearable, and writing becomes a means of coping, if only partially. How do you find solace amid such anguish?

How do you manage comments like, »You're pretty for a Black person« or »I'm not usually into Black people, but you're an exception«? These remarks ignite an inferno within me, and nowadays, I respond with pointed words, even if it risks being labeled as »feisty«. Gone are the days when I would bite my tongue, enduring jokes at my expense. Now, I refuse to remain silent.

And lastly, I must express my gratitude to you for your presence, your unwavering support, resilience, strength, and bravery. Without you by my side, I don't know how I would navigate through these challenges. Together, we find solace, companionship, and fortitude, reminding each other that we will persevere, united and unyielding in the face of adversity.

Don't treat us like we're a freakin' fairground attraction

Can I touch your hair?

If I were granted a penny for every time someone asked, »Can I touch your hair?« I would undoubtedly be a millionaire by now.

Although I can somewhat comprehend the curiosity that fuels such inquiries, I refuse to tolerate the impoliteness, disrespect, and audacity displayed by certain individuals who, without seeking permission, reach out and touch my hair.

Just as I would never dare to randomly inquire if I could touch someone's chest or nose, I view my hair as an intimate extension of myself, mine and mine alone.

In settings like concerts, clubs, or crowded places, I feel my personal space invaded when I suddenly sense fingers delving into my hair.

It's not just a gentle touch; it's an unabashed grasp, akin to a newborn's discovery of its own grip.

Swiftly turning around to confront the offender, I am often met with innocent faces, which only exacerbates the embarrassment I feel.

In those moments, I am left feeling powerless and diminished, my sense of agency stripped away. No one should wield the right to make me feel this way.

So, to those who believe it is acceptable to touch a Black woman's hair without permission, and to anyone who may entertain the urge to do so in the future – I implore you, refrain!

Don't treat us like we're a freakin' fairground attraction!

Moreover, I beseech you to refrain from asking questions or making comments such as, »How do you wash your hair?« or »What kind of comb do you use?«

For in truth, how do you imagine I wash my hair?

With mythical elixirs and magical concoctions? The reality is that, like anyone else, I employ water and shampoo, irrespective of my skin color.

Some questions are dripping with ignorance, so much so that it physically hurts. Google doesn't exist for nothing; it can certainly be used.

My soft, dark skin, once resilient, now craves respite from the relentless gazes laden with hatred. Its protective armor has weakened, and it endures the scorching glares almost daily.

My curly, soft hair, once lustrous, has become vulnerable, succumbing to their ruthless hands that reach down to its roots. Its radiance has dimmed under their unwarranted touch.

My big, tender heart, once full of love, now bears the scars of their hurtful words, distorting its contours. Their malevolent remarks have taken root, embedding themselves, perhaps irrevocably.

If looks could kill

Today unfolded as an absolute disaster, each unfortunate event seeming to conspire against my peace of mind. The morning commenced with my customary green tea, but my fingers betrayed me, causing the cup to fumble from my grasp, spilling its contents all over my desk. The unfortunate mishap didn't end there; the tea cascaded onto my laptop's keyboard, inducing panic as I endeavored to salvage the situation. My anxiety-ridden hands inadvertently sent my laptop crashing to the floor – an exasperating ordeal, to say the least.

As if the morning tribulations weren't enough, my subsequent journey to the laptop repair shop was marred by an encounter with a reckless driver tearing through my otherwise tranquil neighborhood. I admit, I was engrossed in my phone, drawn to a message regarding my seven-year-old nephew's wellbeing. My heart ached for him as I learned of his unfortunate injury, leaving me eager to ascertain the full extent of the incident.

Before I could fully collect my thoughts, I was thrust into the path of a white BMW, its abrupt braking triggering an outpouring of venomous insults from the driver. His final, heinous words, labeling me a »blind little slave girl«, seared into my consciousness like a branding iron.

The hateful tirade paralyzed me, and even as he sped away, I remained rooted to the spot, unable to shake off the shock.

The sting of his words, however, wasn't the sole lingering pain; it was the chilling rage emanating from his icy eyes that haunted me most. My emotions overflowed, betraying my composure, as tears welled up and cascaded down my cheeks.

What had I done to provoke such malevolence? The callous indifference of onlookers added salt to the wounds, none bothering to intervene or check on me despite the driver's boisterous outburst.

Now, back within the confines of my home, my heartbeat gradually steadies, and the remnants of dried tears leave an itch on my cheeks. Seeking solace, I grasp a pen and let my emotions flow onto paper:

My soft, dark skin, once resilient, now craves respite from the relentless gazes laden with hatred. Its protective armor has weakened, and it endures the scorching glares almost daily.

My curly, soft hair, once lustrous, has become vulnerable, succumbing to their ruthless hands that reach down to its roots. Its radiance has dimmed under their unwarranted touch.

My big, tender heart, once full of love, now bears the scars of their hurtful words, distorting its contours. Their malevolent remarks have taken root, embedding themselves, perhaps irrevocably.

The miraculous lotion

Summer 2006: In an exuberant state of mind, completely immersed in the moment, I unleash the chorus of my cherished anthem, amplified by the resounding beat emanating from my trusty waterproof speaker. Though initially hesitant, I now embrace the refreshing chill of the water enveloping my body. My preference typically gravitates toward warm showers, but the current scorching temperatures compel me to alter my habits momentarily. After what seems like an eternity of reveling in the cascading water, I enshroud myself in a snug towel, my melody still resonating through the room as I step out of the tub. As I fervently towel myself dry, an unconscious yearning takes root, clandestinely desiring that the vigorous motion might render my dark skin marginally lighter. I am disheartened by the presence of such thoughts, and yet, I find myself reaching for the tube of bleaching lotion, hesitantly unscrewing the cap and liberally applying it across my body. The lotion emits a subtle fragrance of coconut, its innocent aroma seemingly assuaging my guilt, albeit temporarily. I peer intently at my reflection in the mirror. It has been two weeks since I commenced using this lotion, promising to efface melanin from my skin, and at long last, I perceive a discernible transformation – particularly on my cheeks and forehead, my skin appears visibly lighter. The sensation of elation courses through me, compelling me to twirl about within the expansive confines of my bathroom.

Spring 2014: My hands quiver as I gingerly rest them in my lap, allowing the weight of the question to settle in the room for a fleeting moment. »I suppose«, I begin, my words stumbling over one another, »I wanted to align with the so-called Eurocentric standards of beauty imposed upon society. It wasn't that I wished to be white, but rather, to embody a *more attractive Black*. They incessantly fed me this notion that Black individuals could only be considered beautiful if their skin tone was lighter. I became entangled in this distorted definition of beauty, and even my family unwittingly reinforced it with remarks like 'You've darkened' or 'If you don't start using that miraculous lotion, you'll never find a partner.' When such sentiments echo in your ears since childhood, you inevitably internalize them ...« My voice falters, and Isabel, my therapist, extends a tissue towards me with gentle understanding.

Winter 2022: Today, I embrace my Black skin with unwavering love and proudly display it to the world. However, this journey has been arduous and filled with challenges. It led me through a labyrinth of self-doubt, self-loathing, tears, fury, and profound loneliness. Now, I stand here, my skin just as richly dark as it has always been, unaltered by any skin-lightening lotion. In truth, that »miracle lotion« swiftly lightened my complexion to a point where strangers would inquire about the ethnicity of my parents, assuming one of them must be white. It was then that I realized I was doing a grave disservice to myself and to my heritage. Today, I call upon you to embrace your beautiful skin with boundless pride. No more shame, no more hiding, and no more succumbing to the allure of bleaching. Unapologetically showcase the world your Black skin, wear your battle scars and triumphs with dignity. Let us now resound with fervor, and may our voices never again be hushed to silence!

BRIGITTE LUNGUIEKI MALUNGO

The author was born in Angola in 1989, grew up in Germany, and moved to Spain in 2017. Her 1st book, »Bittersüßes Chaos«, was published in September 2022, followed by her 2nd book, »Meine Haut packt aus«, in January 2023. This secured her 2nd place at the Book Awards in March 2023. After her recent success, she had the honor of hosting readings in Germany, Spain, and Portugal, allowing her to connect with the audience on a deeper level by sharing touching moments of pain, strength, and vulnerability.

Brigitte has been overjoyed by the influx of positive feedback and international interest, which inspired her to release an English version of »Meine Haut packt aus«. She hopes to reach even more people by inviting them to reconsider and reflect on the effects and consequences of racism, as well as to inspire people to contribute to making the world a more peaceful and loving place.

Loved this book?
Why not write your own at story.one?

Let's go!

Milton Keynes UK
Ingram Content Group UK Ltd.
UKHW050131231124
451130UK00020B/25